Shakespeare's
KING LEAR

Shakespeare's

KING LEAR

Crest Publishing House

(A JAICO ENTERPRISE)
G-2, 16 Ansari Road, Darya Ganj
New Delhi-110 002

© Crest Publishing House

No part of this book may be reproduced or utilized in any form or by any means, electronics or mechanical including photocopying, recording or by any information storage and retrieval system, without permission in writing from the publishers.

KING LEAR
ISBN 81-242-0048-3

First Edition : 2000
Reprinted : 2001
Reprinted : 2001
Reprinted : 2002
Reprinted : 2003
Reprinted : 2004

Published by:
CREST PUBLISHING HOUSE
(A Jaico Enterprise)
G-2, 16 Ansari Road, Darya Ganj
New Delhi-110 002

Printed by:
Saurabh Print - O - Pack
A - 16, Sec. 4, Noida

KING LEAR

Lear, King of Britain, had three daughters; Goneril, wife to the Duke of Albany; Regan, wife to the Duke of Cornwall; and Cordelia, a young maid, for whose love the king of France and Duke of Burgundy were joint suitors.

The old king, worn out with age and the fatigues of government, he being more than fourscore years old, determined to take no further part in state affairs, but to leave the management to younger strengths, that he might have time to prepare for death.

With his intent he called his three daughters to him to know from their own lips which of them loved him best, that he might part his kingdom among them in such proportions as their affection for him should seem to deserve.

Goneril, the oldest, declared

that she loved her father more than words could give out, that he was dearer to her than the light of her own eyes, dearer than life and liberty, with a deal of such professing stuff, which is easy to counterfeit where there is no real love, only a few fine words delivered with confidence being wanted in that case.

The king delighted to hear from her own mouth this assurance of her love, and thinking truly that

King Lear called his three daughters

her heart went out with it, in a fit of fatherly fondness bestowed upon her and her husband one third of his ample kingdom.

Then calling to him his second daughter, he demanded what she had to say. Regan, who was made of the same hollow metal as her sister, was not a whit behind in her professions, but rather declared that what her sister had spoken came short of the love which she professed to bear for his highness; insomuch that she found all other joys dead, in comparison with the pleasure which she took in love of her dear king and father.

Lear blessed himself in having such loving children, as he thought; and could do no less, after the handsome assurances which Regan had made, than bestow a third of his kingdom upon her and her husband, equal in size to that which he had already given away to Goneril.

Then turning to his youngest daughter Cordelia, whom he called his joy, he asked what she had to say, thinking no doubt that she would glad his ears with the same loving speeches which her sisters had uttered.

But Cordelia, disgusted with the flattery to her sisters, whose hearts she knew were far from their lips, and seeing that all their coaxing speeches were only intended to wheedle the old king out of his dominions, that they and their husbands might reign in his lifetime, made no other reply but this that she loved his majesty according to her duty, neither more nor less.

The king shocked with this appearance of ingratitude in his favourite child, desired her to consider her words, and to mend her speech, lest it should mar her fortunes.

Cordelia then told her father, that he was her father, that he had given her breeding, and loved her; that she returned those duties back as was most fit, and did obey him, love him, and most honour him. But that she could not frame her mouth to such large speeches as her sisters had done, or promise to love nothing else in the world. Why had her sisters husbands if (as they said) they had no love for anything but their father? If she ever wed, she was sure the lord to whom she gave her hand would want half her love, half of her care and duty; she should never marry like her sisters, to love her father all.

Cordelia, after the crafty flattering speeches of her sisters, which she had seen drawn such extravagant rewards, she thought the handsomest thing she could do was to love and be silent. This put her affection out of suspicion

King Lear told Cordelia to reconsider
her words and mend her speech

of mercenary ends, and showed that she loved, but not for gain.

This plainness of speech, which Lear called pride, so enraged the old monarch that in a fury of resentment he retracted the third part of his kingdom which yet remained, and which he had reserved for Cordelia, and gave it away from her, sharing it equally between her two sisters and their husbands, the Dukes of Albany and Cornwall; whom he now called to him, and in presence of all his courtiers bestowing a coronet between them, invested them jointly with all the power, revenue, and execution of government, only retaining to himself the name of king; all the rest of royalty he resigned; with this reservation, that himself, with a hundred knights for his attendants, was to be maintained by monthly course in each of his daughters' palaces in turn.

So preposterous a disposal of his kingdom, so little guided by reason, and so much by passion, filled all his courtiers with astonishment and sorrow; but none of them had the courage to interpose between this incensed king and his wrath, except the Earl of Kent, who was beginning to speak a good word for Cordelia.

When the passionate Lear on pain of death commanded him to desist; but the good Kent was not

Earl of Kent speaking a good word
for Cordelia to King

so to be repelled. He had been ever loyal to Lear, whom he honoured as a king, loved as a father, followed as a master; and he had never esteemed his life further than as a pawn to wage against his royal master's ene-mies, nor feared to lose it when Lear's safety was the motive; nor now that Lear was most his own enemy, did this faithful servant of the king forget his old principles, but manfully opposed Lear, to do

Lear good; and was unmannerly only because Lear was mad.

The honest freedom of this good Earl of Kent only stirred up the king's wrath the more, and like a frantic patient who kills his physician, and loves his mortal disease, he banished this true servant, and allotted him but five days to make his preparations for departure; but if on the sixth this hated person was found within the realm of Britain, that moment

King Lear banished his true servant
the Earl of Kent

was to be his death. And Kent bade farewell to the king.

The King of France and Duke of Burgundy were now called in to hear the determination of Lear about his youngest daughter, and to know whether they would persist in their courtship to Cordelia, now that she was under her father's displeasure, and had no fortune but her own person to recommend her; and the Duke of Burgundy declined the match and

King of France accepted Cordelia's
hand from her father King Lear

would not take her to wife upon
such conditions; but the king of
France, understanding what the
nature of the fault had been which
had lost her the love of her father,
that it was only a tardiness of
speech, and he not being able to
frame her tongue to flattery like
her sisters, took this young maid
by the hand, and saying that her
virtues were a dowry above a
kingdom, bade Cordelia to take
farewell of her sisters and of her
father, though he had been unkind,

and she should go with him and
be queen of him and of fair
France, and reign over fairer
possessions than her sisters; and
he called the Duke of Burgundy in
contempt a waterish duke, because
his love for this young maid had
in a moment run all away like
water.

Then Cordelia with weeping
eyes took leave of her sisters, and
besought them to love their father
well, and make good their

Cordelia with weeping eyes took leave
of her sisters

professions. And Cordelia with a
heavy heart departed, for she
knew the cunning of her sisters,
and she wished her father in
better hands than she was about
to leave him in.

Cordelia was no sooner gone,
than the devilish dispositions of
her sisters began to show
themselves in their true colours.
Even before the expiration of the
first month, which Lear was to
spend by agreement with his

eldest daughter Goneril, the old king began to find out the differences between promises and performances.

This wretch having got from her father all that he had to bestow, even to the giving away of the crown from off his head, began to grudge even those small remnants of royalty which the old man had reserved to himself, to please his fancy with the idea of being still a king. She could not bear to see him and his hundred knights.

Every time she met her father, she put on a frowning countenance; and when the old man wanted to speak with her, she would feign sickness, or anything to get rid of the sight of him; for it was plain that she esteemed his old age a useless burden, and his attendants an unnecessary expense; not only she herself slackened in her expressions of duty to the king, but by her example, and (it is to be feared) not without her private instructions, her very servants affected to treat him with neglect, and would either refuse to obey his orders, or still more contemptuously pretend not to hear them.

Lear could not but perceive this alternation in the behaviour of his daughter but he shut his eyes against it as long as he could, as people commonly are unwilling to

believe the unpleasant consequences which their own mistakes
and obstinacy have brought upon
them.

True love and fidelity are no
more to be estranged by *ill*, than
falsehood and hollow-heartedness
can be conciliated by *good usage*.
This eminently appears in the
instance of the good Earl of Kent,
who, though banished by Lear
and his life made forfeit if he were
found in Britain, chose to stay and

abide all consequences, as long as there was a chance of his being useful to the king, his master.

In the disguise of a serving man, all his greatness and pomp laid aside, this good Earl proffered his services to the king, who, not knowing him to be Kent in that disguise, but pleased with a certain plainness, or rather bluntness in his answers, which the Earl put on (so different from that smooth oily flattery which he had so much

Earl of Kent in disguise offered his
services to King

reason to be sick of, having found
the effects not answerable in his
daughter), a bargain was quickly
struck, and Lear took Kent into
his service by the name of Caius
as he called himself, never
suspecting him to be his once
great favourite, the high and
mighty Earl of Kent.

This Caius quickly found means
to show his fidelity and love to his
royal master; for Goneril's steward
that same day behaving in a

Earl of Kent laid unmannerly
Goneril's steward on the ground

disrespectful manner to Lear, and giving him saucy looks and language, as no doubt he was secretly encouraged to do by his mistress, Caius not enduring to hear so open an affront put upon his majesty, made no more ado but presently tripped up his heels, and laid the unmannerly slave in the kennel; for which friendly service Lear became more and more attached to him.

The coolness and falling off of

respect which Lear had begun to perceive, were not all which this foolish fond father was to suffer from his unworthy daughter; she now plainly told him that his staying in her palace was inconvenient so long as he insisted upon keeping up an establishment of a hundred knights; that this establishment was useless and expensive, and only served to fill her court with riot and feasting; and she prayed him that he would lessen their number, and keep none but old men about him, such as himself, and fitting his age.

Lear at first could not believe his eyes or ears, nor that it was his daughter who spoke so unkindly. He could not believe that she who had received a crown from him could seek to cut off his train, and grudge him the respect due to his old age. But she, persisting in her undutiful demand, the old man's rage was so excited, that he called her a detested kite, and said that she spoke an untruth; and so indeed she did, for the hundred knights were all men of choice behaviour and sobriety manners, skilled in all particulars of duty, and not given to rioting or feasting, as she said. And he bid his horses to be prepared, for he would go to his other daughter, Regan, he and his hundred knights; and he spoke of ingratitude, and said it was a marble-hearted devil, and showed more hideous in a child than the sea-monster.

And he cursed his eldest daughter Goneril so as was terrible to hear; praying that she might never have a child, or if she had, that it might live to return that scorn and contempt upon her which she had shown to him; that she might feel how sharper than a serpent's tooth it was to have a thankless child. And Goneril's husband, the Duke of Albany, beginning to excuse himself for any share which Lear might suppose he had in the unkindness,

Lear would not hear him out, but in rage ordered his horses to be saddled, and set out with his followers for the abode of Regan, his other daughter. And Lear thought to himself how small the fault of Cordelia (if it was a fault) now appeared, in comparison with her sister's, and he wept, and then he was ashamed that such a creature as Goneril should have so much power over his manhood as to make him weep.

Regan and her husband were keeping their court in great pomp and state at their palace; and Lear despatched his servant Caius with letters to his daughter, that she might be prepared for his reception, while he and his train followed after. But it seems that Goneril had been beforehand with him, sending letters also to Regan, accusing her father of waywardness and ill humours, and advising her not to receive so great a train as he was bringing with him.

This messenger arrived at the same time with Caius, and Caius and he met: and who should it be but Caius's old enemy the steward, whom he had formerly tripped up by the heels for his saucy behaviour to Lear. Caius not liking the fellow's look, and suspecting what he came for, began to revile him, and challenged him to fight, which the fellow refusing, Caius, in a fit of honest passion, beat him soundly, as such a mischiefmaker and carrier of wicked messages deserved; which coming to the ears of Regan and her husband, they ordered Caius to be put in the stocks, though he was a messenger from the king her father, and in that character demanded the highest respect; so that the first thing the king saw when he entered the castle, was his faithful servant Caius sitting in that disgraceful situation.

This was but a bad omen of the
reception which he was to expect;
but a worse followed, when, upon
inquiry for his daughter and her
husband, he was told they were
weary with travelling all night,
and could not see him; and when
lastly, upon his insisting in a
positive and angry manner to see
them, they came to greet him,
whom should he see in their
company, but he hated Goneril,
who had come to tell her own

story, and set her sister against the king her father!

This sight much moved the old man, and still more to see Regan take her by the hand, and he asked Goneril if she was not ashamed to look upon his old white beard. And Regan advised him to go home again with Goneril, and live with her peaceably, dismissing half his attendants, and to ask her forgiveness; for he was old and wanted discretion,

Caius sitting in disgraceful situation

and must be ruled and led by persons that had more discretion than himself. And Lear showed how preposterous that would sound, if he were to go down on his knees, and beg of his own daughter for food and raiment, and he argued against such an unnatural dependence, declaring his resolution never to return with her but to stay where he was with Regan, he and his hundred knights; for he said that she had not forgot the half of the kingdom which he had endowed her with, and that her eyes were not fierce like Goneril's, but mild and kind. And he said that rather than return to Goneril, with half his train cut off, he would go over to France, and beg a wretched pension of the king there, who had married his youngest daughter without a portion.

But he was mistaken in expecting kinder treatment of Regan than he had experienced from her sister Goneril. As if willing to outdo her sister in unfilial behaviour, she declared that she thought fifty knights too many to wait upon him: that five and twenty were enough. Then Lear, nigh heart broken, turned to Goneril, and said that he would go back with her, for her fifty doubled five-and-twenty, and so her love was twice as much as Regan's.

But Goneril excused herself, and said, what need of so many as

five-and-twenty? or even ten? or
five? when he might be waited by
her servants, or her sister's
servants? So these two wicked
daughters, as if they strove to
exceed each other in cruelty to
their old father, who had been so
good to them, by little and little
would have abated him of all his
train, all respect (little enough for
him that once commanded a
kingdom), which was left him to
show that he had once been a
king! Not that a splendid train is

essential to happiness, but from a king to a beggar is a hard change, from commanding millions to be without one attendant; and it was the ingratitude in his daughter's denying it, more than what he would suffer by the want of it, which pierced this poor king to the heart; insomuch, that with this double ill usage, and vexation for having so foolishly given away a kingdom, his wits began to be unsettled, and while he said he knew not what, he vowed revenge

against those unnatural hags, and
to make examples of them that
should be a terror to the earth!

While he was thus idly
threatening what his weak arm
could never execute, night came
on, and a loud storm of thunder
and lightning with rain; and his
daughters still persisting in their
resolution not to admit his
followers, he called for his horses
and chose rather to encounter the
utmost fury of the storm abroad,

than stay under the same roof
with these ungrateful daughters;
and they, saying that the injuries
which wilful men procure to themselves are their just punishment,
suffered him to go in that condition
and shut their doors upon him.

The winds were high, and the
rain and storm increased, when
the old man sallied forth to combat
with the elements, less sharp
than his daughters' unkindness.
For many miles about there was

scarce a bush; and there upon a heath, exposed to the fury of the storm in a dark night, did king Lear wander out, and defy the winds and thunder; and he bid the winds to blow the earth into the sea or swell the waves of the sea till they drowned the earth, that no token might remain of any such ungrateful animal as man.

The old king was now left with no other companion than the poor fool, who still abided with him, with his merry conceits striving to outjest misfortune, saying it was but a naughty night to swim in, and truly the king had better go in and ask his daughter's blessings:

But he that has a little tiny wit,
With heigh ho, the wind and the rain!
Must make content with his fortunes fit,
Though the rain it raineth every day:

King Lear combating storm

and swearing it was a brave night to cool a lady's pride.

Thus poorly accompanied, this once great monarch was found by his ever faithful servant the good Earl of Kent, now transformed to Caius, who ever followed close at his side, though the king did not know him to be the Earl; and he said," Alas! sir, are you here? creatures that love night, love not such nights as these. This dreadful storm has driven the beasts to their hiding places; Man's nature cannot endure the affliction or the fear," And Lear rebuked him and said, these lesser evils were not felt, where a greater malady was fixed.

When the mind is at ease, the body has leisure to be delicate, but the tempest in his mind did take all feeling else from his senses, but of that which beat at his heart. And he spoke of filial ingratitude, and said it was all one as if the mouth should tear the hand for lifting food to it; for parents were hands and food and everything to children.

But the good Caius still persisting in his entreaties that the king would not stay out in the open air, at last persuaded him to enter a little wretched hovel which stood upon the heath, where the fool first entering, suddenly ran back terrified, saying that he had seen a spirit.

Caius persuading King to enter a
little wretched hovel

But upon examination this spirit proved to be nothing more than a poor Bedlam beggar, who had crept into this deserted hovel for shelter, and with his talk about devils frightened the fool, one of those poor lunatics who are either mad or feign to be so, the better to extort charity from the compassionate country people, who go about the country, calling themselves poor Tom and ˙poor Turlygood, saying, "Who gives anything to poor Tom?" sticking pins and nails nd sprigs of rosemary into their arms to make them bleed; and with such horrible actions, partly by prayers, and partly with lunatic curses, they move or terrify the ignorant country-folks into giving them alms.

This poor fellow was such a one; and the king seeing him in so wretched a plight, with nothing but a blanket about his loins to cover his nakedness, could not be persuaded but that the fellow was some father who had given all away to his daughters, and brought himself to that pass; for nothing he thought could bring a man to such wretchedness but the having unkind daughters.

And from this and many such wild speeches which he uttered, the good Caius plainly perceived that he was not in his perfect mind, but that his daughters' ill usage had really made him go mad. And now the loyalty of this worthy Earl of Kent showed itself in more essential services than he had hitherto found opportunity to perform.

For with the assistance of some of the king's attendants who remained loyal, he had the person of his royal master removed at day-break to the castle of Dover, where his own friends and influence, as Earl of Kent, chiefly lay; and himself embarking for

France, hastened to the court of Cordelia, and did there in such moving terms represent the pitiful condition of her royal father, and set out in such lively colours the inhumanity of her sisters, that this good and moving child with many tears besought the king her husband that he would give her leave to embark for England, with a sufficient power to subdue these cruel daughters and their husbands, and restore the old king her father to his throne;

which being granted, she set forth, and with a royal army landed at Dover.

Lear having by some chance escaped from the guardians which the good Earl of Kent had put over him to take care of him in his lunacy, was found by some of Cordelia's train, wandering about the fields near Dover, in a pitiable condition, stark mad and singing aloud to himself, with a crown upon his head which he had made

King Lear wandering about fields
near Dover in a pitiable condition

of straw and nettles, and other wild weeds that he had picked up in the corn-fields.

By the advice of the physicians, Cordelia though earnestly desirous of seeing her father, was prevailed upon to put off the meeting, till by sleep and the operation of harbs which they gave him, he should be restored to greater composure. By the aid of these skilful physicians, to whom Cordelia promised all her gold and jewels for the recovery of the old king, Lear was soon in a condition to see his daughter.

A tender sight it was to see the meeting between this father and daughter; to see the struggles between the joy of this poor old king at beholding again his once darling child, and the shame at receiving such filial kindness from her whom he had cast off for so small a fault in his displeasure; both these passions struggling with the remains of his malady,

King Lear receiving Kindness from
her daughter Cordelia

which in his half-crazed brain
sometimes made him that he
scarce remembered where he was,
or who it was that so kindly kissed
him and spoke to him: and then
he would beg the standers-by not
to laugh at him if he were mistaken
in thinking this lady to be his
daughter Cordelia!

And then to see him fall on his
knees to beg pardon of his child;
and she, good lady, kneeling all
the while to ask a blessing of him,

and telling him that it did not become him to kneel, but it was her duty, for she was his child, his true and very child Cordelia! and she kissed him (as she said) to kiss away all her sisters' unkindness, and said that they might be ashamed of themselves, to turn their old kind father with his white beard out into the cold air, when her enemy's dog, though it had bit her (as she prettily expressed it), should have stayed by her fire such a night as that, and warmed himself.

And she told her father how she had come from France with purpose to bring him assistance; and he said that she must forget and forgive, for he was old and foolish, and did not know what he did; but that to be sure she had great cause not to love him, but her sisters had none. And Cordelia said that she had no cause, no more than they had.

So we will leave this old king in the protection of his dutiful and loving child, where, by the help of sleep and medicine, she and her physicians at length succeeded in winding up the untuned and jarring senses which the cruelty of his other daughters had so violently shaken. Let us return to say a word or two about those cruel daughters.

These monsters of ingratitude, who had been so false to their old father, could not be expected to prove more faithful to their own husbands. They soon grew tired of paying even the appearance of duty and affection, and in an open way showed they had fixed their loves upon another. It happened that object of their guilty loves was the same.

It was Edmund, a natural son of the late Earl of Gloucester, who by his treacheries had succeeded in disinheriting his brother Edgar, the lawful heir, from his earldom, and by his wicked practices was now Earl himself; a wicked man, and a fit object for the love of such wicked creatures as Goneril and Regan.

It falling out about this time that the Duke of Cornwall, Regan's husband, died, Regan's immediately declared her intention of wedding this Earl of Gloucester, which rousing the jealousy of her sister, to whom as well as to Regan this wicked Earl had at sundry times professed love, Goneril found means to make away with her sister by poison; but being detected in her practices and imprisoned by her husband, the Duke of Albany, for this deed, and for her guilty passion for the Earl which had come to his ears, she, in a fit of disappointed love and rage, shortly put an end to her own life. Thus the justice of Heaven at last overtook these wicked daughters.

While the eyes of all men were

upon this event, admiring the justice displayed in their deserved deaths, the same eyes were suddenly taken off from this sight to admire at the mysterious ways of the same power in the melancholy fate of the young and virtuous daughter, the Lady Cordelia whose good deeds did seem to deserve a more fortunate conclusion; but it is an awful truth, that innocence and piety are not always successful in this world.

The forces which Goneril and Regan had sent out under the command of the bad Earl of Gloucester were victorious and Cordelia, by the practices of this wicked Earl, who did not like that any one should stand between him and the throne, ended his life in prison. Thus, Heaven took this innocent lady to itself in her young years, after showing world an illustrious example of filial duty. Lear did not long survive this kind child.

Before he died, the good Earl of Kent, who had still attended his old master's steps from the first of his daughters' ill usage to this sad period of his decay, tried to make him understand that it was he who had followed him under the name of Caius; but Lear's care-crazed brain at that time could not comprehend how that could be, or how Kent and Caius could be the same person; so Kent thought it needless to trouble him with explanations at such a time;

Duke of Albany seeing the dead body
of her wife Goneril

and Lear soon after expiring, this faithful servant to the king, between age and grief for his old master's vexations, soon followed him to the grave.

How the judgement of Heaven overtook the bad Earl of Gloucester, whose treasons were discovered, and himself slain in single combat with his brother, the lawful Earl and how Goneril's husband, the Duke of Albany, who was innocent of the death of

Cordelia, and had never encouraged his lady in her wicked proceedings against her father, ascended the throne of Britain after the death of Lear, is needless here to narrate; Lear and his three daughters being dead, whose adventures alone concern our story.

THE OTHER BOOKS IN
THIS SERIES ARE

Shakespeare's

- The Comedy of Errors
- Hamlet
- Romeo and Juliet
- The Merchant of Venice
- Macbeth
- A Midsummer Night's Dream
- Othello
- Much Ado About Nothing
- As You Like It
- Twelfth Night or What You Will
- The Tempest

ESSENCE SERIES
from
CREST PUBLISHING HOUSE

- The Essence of Hinduism
- The Essence of Self Improvement
- The Essence of Relaxation
- The Essence of Happiness
- The Essence of Thoughts
- The Essence of Success
- The Essence of Beauty